Bond Assessment Papers

First papers in Mathematics

J M Bond and Andrew Baines

Key words

Some special maths words are used in this book. You will find them in **bold** the first time they appear in the papers. These words are explained here.

bar chart   a chart that records information in bars (see page 11)

capacity   how much liquid a container will hold. Capacity is usually measured in litres and millitres.

digit   any single number: e.g. 4 has one digit, 37 has two, 437 has three

even numbers   numbers that can be divided by two: 2, 4, 6, 8 are even numbers

fraction   a part of a whole, written like this: $\frac{1}{2}$, $\frac{1}{4}$, $\frac{2}{3}$.

$\frac{2}{3}$ means two parts out of three.

frequency table   a table that records the number of times something happens (see the frequency table on page 5)

mirror line   the line in which a shape can be reflected, like the reflection in a mirror

multiple   a number which another number multiplies into: 3, 6, 9, 12, 15, 60, 93 are multiples of 3

number track   a continuous strip of numbers for counting along (see page 20)

odd numbers   numbers that cannot be divided by two: 1, 3, 5, 7, 9 are odd numbers

pictogram   a diagram that records something using pictures (see page 37)

prism   a shape which has the same section all the way through, e.g. a 'tent' shape is a triangular prism

product   the answer when you multiply two numbers together: the product of 4 and 2 is 8

quadrilateral   any shape with four straight sides

rectangle, rectangular   a quadrilateral with square corners, usually with two short sides and two long sides

round down, round up   round means roughly or approximately. 42 rounded down to the nearest 10 is 40. 47 rounded up to the nearest 10 is 50

standard units of measure   e.g kilogram (kg), gram (g), metre (m), millimetre (mm)
The following are not standard units of measure: cupful, handful

sum   the answer when you add two numbers together:

the sum of 2 and 4 is 6

symmetry   a shape has symmetry if it has one or more mirror lines, like this:

Venn diagram   a chart for sorting information of different kinds (see page 19)

vertex, vertices   the corner or point of a shape, where its sides or faces meet. The arrows are pointing to the vertices on these two shapes.

Paper 1

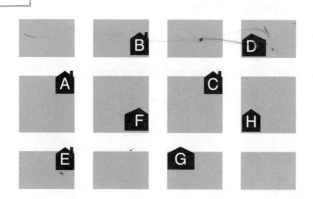

N
W E
S

Answer the following using either: North (N), South (S), East (E) or West (W).

1 House C is _East_ of house A.

2 Shop F is _west_ of newsagents H.

3 School G is _east_ and South of house A.

4–5 Shop D is _north_ and _west_ of house E.

6–7 House C is _north_ and _west_ of house B. X

8–9 House E is _north_ and _west_ of house B. X

10–11 School G is _north_ and _west_ of Shop D. X

Class 3B made a weather chart for the first 4 weeks of the term.

They drew if it was sunny, if it rained and if it was dull.

1st week						
2nd week						
3rd week						
4th week						

12 In the first week how many days did it rain?

13 In the second week how many days were sunny?

14 In the third week how many days were dull?

15 In the fourth week how many days did it not rain?

2
3
2
6

16 How many days were sunny in total?

17 How many days were rainy in total?

18 How many days were dull in total?

Draw in the missing shape on each of the following patterns.

19

20 50p 20p 10p 50p 20p 10p

21

22

23 10:20 20:10 10:20 20:10 10:20 20:10

24

6

How many minutes are there between:

25 (10:00) and (10:30)   _30_ minutes

26 (10:40) and (10:55)   _15_ minutes

27 (11:10) and (11:30)   _20_ minutes   3

28 53 subtract 30 equals   23

29 100 less than 452 is   352

30 Which is more: 132 cm or 123 cm?   132cm   3

4

30
TOTAL

Paper 2

Here is a **frequency table** showing a class's favourite wild animals.

Favourite animal	Votes
Lion	6
Elephant	9
Giraffe	5
Zebra	3
Tiger	4

1 How many children voted for lion? _____

2 How many children voted for elephant? _____

3 How many children voted for zebra? _____

4 How many children voted for giraffe? _____

5 How many children voted for tiger? _____

6 How many more children voted for elephant than zebra? _____

7 How many more children voted for lion than giraffe? _____   7

This sign   <   means less than and this sign   >   means greater than.
Put one of these signs in each of the spaces below.

8 23 _____ 24   9 17 _____ 16

10 21 _____ 19   11 10 _____ 9

12 12 _____ 14   13 18 _____ 81   6

Write the answers to these sums.

14   14   15   12
       + 17   + 27
       ____   ____

       ____   ____

16   15   17   37
       + 15   − 14
       ____   ____

       ____   ____

5

18   47
       − 22
       ———

19   62
       − 32
       ———

`6`

20–22 Write down what numbers are coming out of the factory.

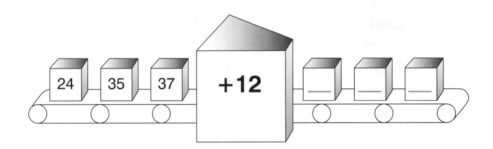

`3`

23 How many times can I take 6 from 18?   ———

24 I share 16 apples among 4 children.
How many apples will each child have?   ———

`2`

Look at this diagram.

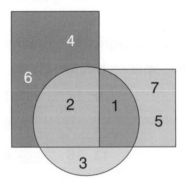

25 What is the **sum** of all the numbers in the square?   ———

26 What is the sum of all the numbers in the circle?   ———

27 What is the sum of all the numbers in the rectangle?   ———

28 Which number is in the square and the circle?   ———

`4`

29–30 Ring the numbers which are **multiples** of 10.

      63   4   30   26   40

`2`

`30`
TOTAL

Paper 3

1–10 Complete the Carroll diagram below.

Multiples of 3 up to 31	
Even	**Odd**

11 How many multiples of 12 are there in your table? _____

12 What is 57 to the nearest 10? _____

13 What is 85 to the nearest 10? _____

14 What is 12 to the nearest 10? _____

15 What is 567 to the nearest 100? _____

16 Write the correct number in the box.

67 $\longrightarrow$
10 more is

17 Write the correct number in the box.

$\longrightarrow$ 89
10 less is

18 Write the correct number in the box.

89 $\longrightarrow$
20 less is

What time do these clocks show?

19

_____

20

_____

21

_____

22

_____

23

_____

24

_____

25 17 + 6 = _____

26 37 + 6 = _____

27 67 + 6 = _____

28 87 + 6 = _____

29 How many 4s are there in 20?

30 How many 7s are there in 63?

6

4

_____

2

_____

30
TOTAL

Paper 4

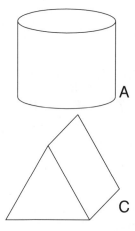 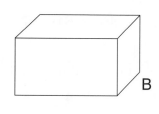 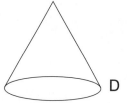

1 Which shape is not a **prism**? _____

2–3 Which two shapes have more than one **vertex**? _____ and _____

4 Which shape has only 3 **rectangular** sides? _____

5 Name shape D. _____

5

How many tens are there in each of these numbers?

6 90 = _____ tens

7 180 = _____ tens

8 160 = _____ tens

9 130 = _____ tens

10 210 = _____ tens

5

Write the answers to these questions.

11
$$\begin{array}{r} 8 \\ \times\ 5 \\ \hline \\ \hline \end{array}$$

12
$$\begin{array}{r} 7 \\ \times\ 5 \\ \hline \\ \hline \end{array}$$

13
$$\begin{array}{r} 6 \\ \times\ 6 \\ \hline \\ \hline \end{array}$$

14
$$\begin{array}{r} 5 \\ \times\ 4 \\ \hline \\ \hline \end{array}$$

4

15–16 Ring the odd numbers.

46   49   55   58   62   74   80

17–18 Ring the even numbers.

46   49   55   58   61   73   81

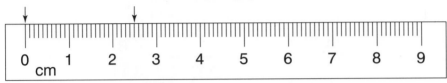

19 What is the length shown on the ruler? _____ cm

20 What is the weight shown on the scales? _____ kg

21 What is the **capacity** of the jug? _____ ml

Suggest the best **standard unit of measure** for the following by choosing from km, kg, l or m:

22 how much water is in a bath _____

23 how heavy a car is _____

24 distance from New York to Paris _____

25 the length of a football pitch _____

26–30 Work out how much was in each person's change box.

Name	Number of 5p coins	Number of 2p coins	Number of 1p coins	Total in the change box
Patrick	4	3	2	
David	2	4	3	
Richard	6	1	2	
Terry	5	3	1	
Karen	3	3	3	

4

3

4

5

30
TOTAL

Paper 5

Here is a **bar chart** showing the favourite colours of a group of children.

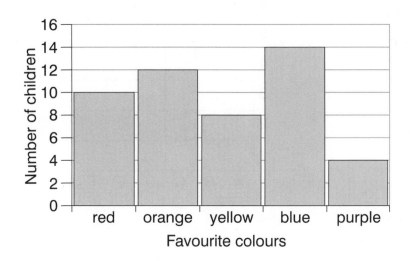

Favourite colours

1 What was the least popular colour? _____

2 What was the third most popular colour? _____

3 How many children voted for purple? _____

4 How many children voted for yellow and orange? _____

`4`

5 What is 138 to the nearest 100? _____

6 What is 394 to the nearest 100? _____

7 The TV programme lasted 28 minutes, which is ____ min to the nearest 10 min.

8 The computer keyboard is 33 cm long, which is ____ cm to the nearest 10 cm.

`4`

9–13 Write the missing number in each space below.

36	33	30	____	24	21	18
74	73	72	71	70	____	68
97	87	77	67	____	47	37
24	26	____	30	32	34	36
26	24	22	20	____	16	14

`5`

14–19 Here is the plan of a classroom. It has been divided into squares. Show where each child sits by writing the first letter of each child's name in the correct square on the plan.

Terry sits in D6.

Alan sits in B3.

Carol sits in E1.

Rafiq sits in A5.

Lulu sits in F4.

Giles sits in C2.

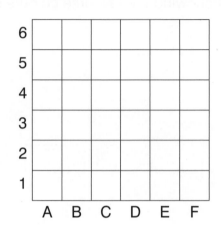

6

Look at this example.

♦ = 8 ÷ 4

♦ = 2

Now do these.

20 ♣ = 5 + 6

♣ = _____

21 ♥ = 3 × 3

♥ = _____

22 ♠ = 1 + 2 + 3

♠ = _____

23 • = 7 − 1

• = _____

24 Φ = 10 − 2 − 1

Φ = _____

25 ♣ = 8 ÷ 2

♣ = _____

6

Underline the correct answer in each line.

26   18 + 8 =   16   28   26   36

27   23 − 8 =   31   15   13   14

28   £1.00 − 20p =   120p   60p   70p   80p

29 $\frac{1}{2}$ of 8 =   4   16   3   28

30   3 + 4 + 5 = 11   12   13   10

5

12

30
TOTAL

Paper 6

This sign < means less than and this sign > means greater than.

Put one of these signs in each of the spaces below.

1 11 _____ 10

2 17 _____ 23

3 6 _____ 60

4 8 _____ (2 × 3)

5 7 _____ (10 − 1)

6 Michael is leaving school. What time is it?   _____ : _____ p.m.

7 Michael is going out to play. What time is it?   _____ : _____ p.m.

8 Michael is eating his dinner. What time is it?   _____ : _____ p.m.

9 How long is it since he left school?   _____ hr _____ min

10 Michael is having a shower. What time is it?   _____ : _____ p.m.

11–16 Which numbers are coming out of these factories?

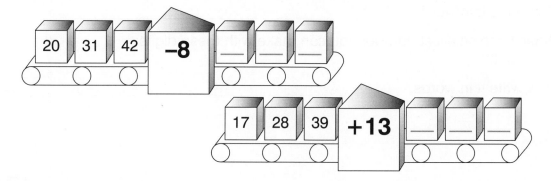

The following numbers are written in words.

Write them in figures.

17 One hundred and one _____

18 Two hundred and twenty _____

19 Eighty-nine _____

20 Four hundred and forty-four _____

21 Three hundred and eleven _____

22 One hundred and ten _____ `6`

23–24 Draw the lines of **symmetry** (**mirror lines**) in these shapes.

`2`

25 What is the biggest number you can make with these **digits**: 2, 3, 4? _____

26 Now write it in words. _____

27 What is the smallest number you can make with these digits: 3, 5, 4? _____

28 Now write it in words. _____

29 What is the smallest number you can make with these digits: 9, 5, 8? _____

30 Now write it in words. _____ `6`

`30` TOTAL

Paper 7

Boys

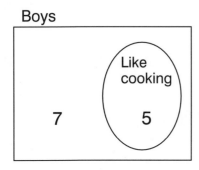

Girls

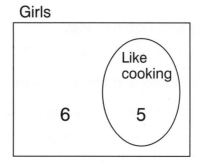

1   How many boys like cooking? ....

2   How many girls like cooking? ....

3   How many boys don't like cooking? ....

4   How many girls don't like cooking? ....

5   How many boys and girls like cooking? ....

6   How many boys and girls don't like cooking? .... | 6 |

7   Find a pair of numbers with a sum of 5 and a **product** of 4.

_1_   and _____

8–9   Find a pair of numbers with a sum of 5 and a product of 6.

_____ and _____

10–11   Find a pair of numbers with a sum of 11 and a product of 30.

_____ and _____

12–13   Find a pair of numbers with a sum of 19 and a product of 34.

_____ and _____ | 7 |

Underline the correct answer in each line.

14   5 + 2 + 6 =   11   12   13   14

15   6 × 10 =   16   60   600   66 | 2 |

15

16 Maria had 7 sweets, Kim had 3 sweets and Sara had 8 sweets.

They put them all together and then shared them equally.

How many sweets does each girl have now? _____

17 I have 39p. How much more do I need to buy a book
costing 50p? _____ p

18 Bill has 14p and Bob has 23p.

How much more has Bob than Bill? _____ p

19 Write two hundred and two in figures. _____

20 Andrew has 1p more than Simon, who has 5p.

How much money do they have altogether? _____ p   5

Last Tuesday Jason got up at 8 a.m. and went to bed at 8 p.m.

Here is a bar chart which shows how he spent the day.

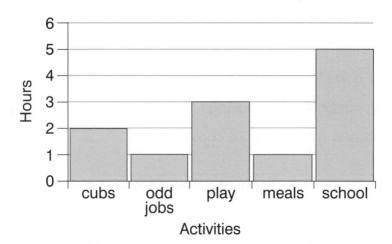

21 How long was Jason at school? _____

22 How long did he play? _____

23 How long did he spend eating? _____

24 How long did he spend at Cubs? _____

25 How long was he doing odd jobs? _____

26 How many hours did he spend out of bed? _____   6

27   20
      – 13
      ———
      ———

28   30
      – 14
      ———
      ———

29   20
      – 11
      ———
      ———

30   30
      – 16
      ———
      ———

TOTAL 30

Paper 8

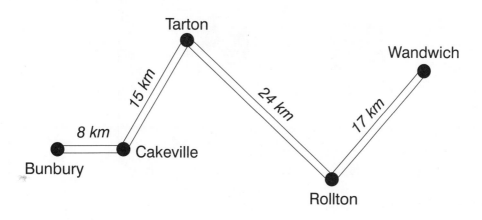

1 How far is it from Bunbury to Tarton?   _____ km

2 From Tarton to Wandwich is   _____ km

3 Cakeville is _____ km closer to Bunbury than it is to Tarton.

4 Rollton is _____ km closer to Wandwich than it is to Tarton.

5 How far is it from Bunbury to Rollton?   _____ km

6 How far is it from Wandwich to Cakeville?   _____ km

7 How far is it from Rollton to Cakeville?   _____ km

8–9 Which two towns are nearest to each other? _____ and _____

9

10 How many 6s are there in 120? _____

11 How much smaller is 27 than 80? _____

12 How much have I altogether if I have £1.00, 25p and £3.10? _____

13 If I make 75 three times as big, what number will it be? _____

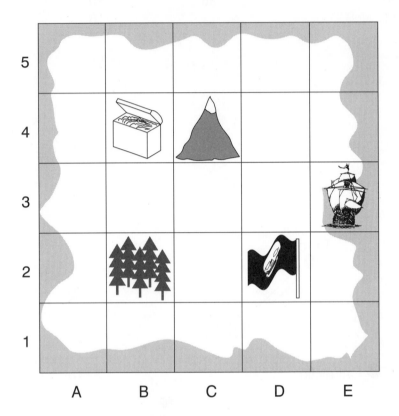

There is a flag on the island at D2.

14 Where has the pirate ship landed? _____

15 Where is the forest? _____

16 Where is the mountain? _____

17 Where is the treasure? _____

18 Mark a big X in the middle of C3.

Use North (N), South (S), East (E) or West (W) to complete the following sentences.

19 The treasure is _____ of the mountain.

20 The treasure is _____ of the forest.

21 The flag is _____ of the forest.

Write the missing number in each space below.

22	4	8	12	_____	20
23	15	_____	9	6	3
24	5	10	15	_____	25
25	24	_____	16	12	8

4

26–30 A train takes 1 hr 5 min to travel from Coldville to Warmwich.

Fill in this chart.

Leaves Coldville	06:00	07:05	08:15	09:35	10:55
Arrives Warmwich					

5

30 TOTAL

Paper 9

1–6 Put the letters **a** to **f** in the correct place in the **Venn diagram**.

Shapes

Right-angled shapes

a

b

c

d

e

f

7 Shape **c** is called a _____

7

Fill in the missing number in each space below.

8	6	9	12	15	_____
9	80	90	_____	110	120

Write the answers to these sums.

10
$$\begin{array}{r} £\,1.20 \\ +\ £\,2.35 \\ \hline \end{array}$$

11
$$\begin{array}{r} £\,1.05 \\ +\ £\,2.06 \\ \hline \end{array}$$

12
$$\begin{array}{r} £\,2.12 \\ +\ £\,1.21 \\ \hline \end{array}$$

13
$$\begin{array}{r} £\,3.02 \\ +\ £\,1.08 \\ \hline \end{array}$$

14–15 Here is part of a **number track**. Write 254 and 243 on it.

				247	248	249					

16–17 Here is part of a number track. Write 583 and 582 on it.

				586	587	588					

18–19 Ring the odd numbers.

26   79   35   58   92   14   60

20–21 Ring the even numbers.

25   59   15   38   61   73   90

20

2

4

4

4

Here is a chart some boys made.

It shows their heights.

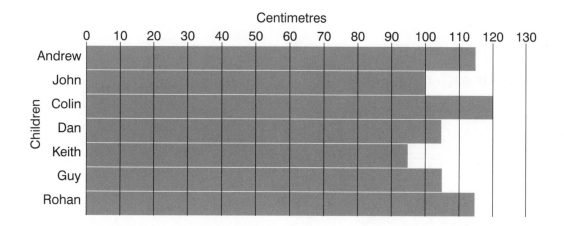

22-23 Name two boys who are the same height and are 115 cm tall.

_____ and _____

24-25 Name two boys who are 105 cm tall. _____ and _____

26 Who is the tallest boy? _____

27 How tall is he? _____

28 Who is the shortest boy? _____

29 Keith is _____ cm shorter than Colin.

30 How many boys are less than 110 cm tall? _____

9

30
TOTAL

Paper 10

January is the 1st month	July is the 7th month
February is the 2nd month	August is the 8th month
March is the 3rd month	September is the 9th month
April is the 4th month	October is the 10th month
May is the 5th month	November is the 11th month
June is the 6th month	December is the 12th month

1st of November 1993 can be written as 1.11.93.

Here are some birthdays written this way.

Anna was born   20.10.95
Carl was born   21.2.92
Karen was born 23.8.94
Martin was born 24.5.93

In which month was each child born?

1 Anna   _____

2 Carl   _____

3 Karen   _____

4 Martin   _____

5 _____ is the eldest.

6 _____ is the youngest.

Here is an easy way to add up three numbers which come after each other.

1 + **2** + 3 =   6 which is the same as   3 × **2** = 6
5 + **6** + 7 = 18 which is the same as   3 × **6** = 18

Now do these in the same way.

7 2 + 3 + 4 =   _____

8 9 + 10 + 11 =   _____

9 4 + 5 + 6 =   _____

10 6 + 7 + 8 =   _____

11 12 + 11 + 10 =   _____

12 7 + 8 + 9 =   _____

13 If Jack was 4 years older he would be the same age as Jill.

Jill is 13. How old is Jack?   _____ years

14 Add together 4 and 7 and then take 5 from your answer.

How many do you have now?   _____

Can you complete these bills for the baker? Write your answers in £.

Fruit cake £3.50

Cream buns 35p

Cream sponge £1.35

Mince pies 25p

15–18
Mrs Smith bought:

	£	p
2 mince pies		___
1 cream sponge		___
1 cream bun		___
Total		___

19–22
Mrs Jones bought:

	£	p
2 cream buns		___
1 fruit cake		___
1 mince pie		___
Total		___

23–27
Mr Green bought:

	£	p
1 fruit cake		___
1 cream sponge		___
1 mince pie		___
1 cream bun		___
Total		___

13

Measure the lengths of these things.

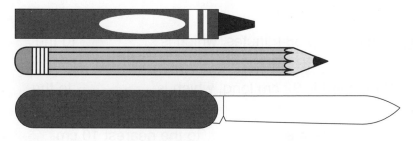

28 The crayon is _____ cm long.

29 The pencil is _____ cm long.

30 The penknife is _____ cm long.

3

30
TOTAL

Paper 11

Here is a chart showing how much money some children spent on sweets yesterday.

Each square represents 5p.

Sam												
Amy												
Mark												
Simon												
Jessica												
Helen												

1 How much did Sam spend? _____

2 How much did Amy spend? _____

3 Mark spent _____

4 Simon spent _____

5 Jessica spent _____

6 Helen spent _____

7 How much more did Sam spend than Jessica? _____

8 How much more did Simon spend than Amy? _____

8

9 What is 394 to the nearest 100? _____

10 What is 138 to the nearest 100? _____

11 The TV programme lasted 38 minutes, which is _____ to the nearest 10 min.

12 The computer keyboard is 32 cm long, which is _____ to the nearest 10 cm.

13 Two computer keyboards are _____ to the nearest 10 cm.

5

14 Draw a line under any number that is a multiple of 3 but not 5.

       28   35   36   25   15

Paper 1

1 E
2 W
3 E
4 N
5 E
6 S
7 E
8 S
9 W
10 S
11 W
12 2
13 3
14 2
15 6
16 14
17 6
18 8
19
20
21
22
23 10:20
24
25 30
26 15
27 20
28 23
29 352
30 132

Paper 2

1 6
2 9
3 3
4 5
5 4
6 6
7 1
8 <
9 >
10 >
11 >
12 <
13 <
14 31
15 39
16 30
17 23
18 25
19 30
20 36
21 47
22 49
23 3
24 4
25 13
26 6
27 12
28 1
29 30
30 40

Paper 3

1 6 even
2 12 even
3 18 even
4 24 even
5 30 even
6 3 odd
7 9 odd
8 15 odd
9 21 odd
10 27 odd
11 2
12 60
13 90
14 10
15 600
16 77
17 99
18 69
19 2 o'clock
20 5 o'clock
21 half past 1
22 half past 10
23 11 o'clock
24 10 o'clock
25 23
26 43
27 73
28 93
29 5
30 9

Answers

A1

Paper 4

1. D
2. B
3. C
4. C
5. cone
6. 9
7. 18
8. 16
9. 13
10. 21
11. 40
12. 35
13. 36
14. 20
15. 49
16. 55
17. 46
18. 58
19. 2.5
20. 4.5
21. 1000
22. litres
23. kg
24. km
25. m
26. 28p
27. 21p
28. 34p
29. 32p
30. 24p

Paper 5

1. purple
2. red
3. 4
4. 20
5. 100
6. 400
7. 30
8. 30
9. 27
10. 69

11. 57
12. 28
13. 18

14–19

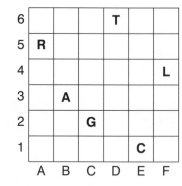

20. 11
21. 9
22. 6
23. 6
24. 7
25. 4
26. 26
27. 15
28. 80p
29. 4
30. 12

Paper 6

1. >
2. <
3. <
4. >
5. <
6. 3:35
7. 5:05
8. 6:00
9. 2 hr 25 min
10. 7:20
11. 12
12. 23
13. 34
14. 30
15. 41
16. 52
17. 101

18. 220
19. 89
20. 444
21. 311
22. 110

23.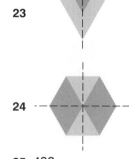

24.

25. 432
26. four hundred and thirty-two
27. 345
28. three hundred and forty-five
29. 589
30. five hundred and eighty-nine

Paper 7

1. 5
2. 5
3. 7
4. 6
5. 10
6. 13
7. 4
8. 2
9. 3
10. 5
11. 6
12. 2
13. 17
14. 13
15. 60
16. 6
17. 11
18. 9

19 202
20 11
21 5 hr
22 3 hr
23 1 hr
24 2 hr
25 1 hr
26 12 hr
27 7
28 16
29 9
30 14

Paper 8

1 23
2 41
3 7
4 7
5 47
6 56
7 39
8 Bunbury
9 Cakeville
10 20
11 53
12 £4.35
13 225
14 E3
15 B2
16 C4
17 B4

18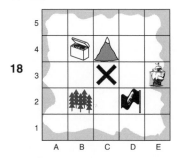

19 W
20 N
21 E
22 16

23 12
24 20
25 20
26 07:05
27 08:10
28 09:20
29 10:40
30 12:00

Paper 9

1–6

Shapes

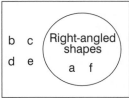

7 rectangle
8 18
9 100
10 £3.55
11 £3.11
12 £3.33
13 £4.10

14–15

243			247	248	249				254

16–17

582	583		586	587	588				

18 79
19 35
20 38
21 90
22 Andrew
23 Rohan
24 Dan
25 Guy
26 Colin
27 120 cm
28 Keith
29 25 cm
30 4 boys

Paper 10

1 October
2 February
3 August
4 May
5 Carl
6 Anna
7 9
8 30
9 15
10 21
11 33
12 24
13 9
14 6
15 £0.50
16 £1.35
17 £0.35
18 £2.20
19 £0.70
20 £3.50
21 £0.25
22 £4.45
23 £3.50
24 £1.35
25 £0.25
26 £0.35
27 £5.45
28 6.5
29 8.5
30 10.5

Paper 11

1 55p
2 20p
3 30p
4 45p
5 25p
6 30p
7 30p
8 25p
9 400
10 100
11 40 min
12 30 cm
13 60 cm
14 36
15 15
16 300
17 40
18 60
19 5
20 75p or £0.75
21 £3.75
22 1994
23 6
24 3
25 5
26 7
27 11:15
28 10:30
29 7:45
30 12.10

Paper 12

1 500
2 2
3 800
4 C
5 D
6 5
7 97
8 67
9 87
10 46
11 55
12 35
13 10 + 1
14 6 − 4
15 2 + 1
16 2 × 1
17 50
18 70
19 60
20 3
21 5
22 5
23 4
24 6
25 5
26 4
27 2
28 3 and 6
29 1 and 11
30 6 and 6

Paper 13

1–7

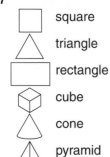

square

triangle

rectangle

cube

cone

pyramid

cuboid

8 43
9 23
10 77
11 17
12 53
13 31
14 +
15 −
16 ×

17

18

19

20 2000
21 $\frac{1}{4}$
22 $\frac{3}{4}$
23 $\frac{3}{4}$
24 $\frac{1}{4}$
25 $\frac{1}{2}$
26 $\frac{1}{2}$
27 $\frac{1}{2}$

28 $\frac{1}{2}$
29 247
30 two hundred and forty-seven

Paper 14

1 104
2 90
3 108
4 95
5 102
6 135
7 8
8 10
9 10
10 5
11 5
12 3
13 10
14 35
15 999
16 3
17 5
18 2
19 4
20 19
21 15
22 7.5 cm
23 11 cm
24 12 cm
25 5.5 cm
26 9 cm
27 10.5 cm
28 25
29 102
30 120

Paper 15

1 20
2 100
3 20
4 10
5 $\frac{1}{2}$
6 $\frac{1}{2}$
7 $\frac{1}{4}$
8 $\frac{3}{4}$
9 $\frac{1}{2}$
10 $\frac{1}{2}$
11 $\frac{1}{2}$
12 $\frac{1}{2}$
13 ×
14 −
15 ×
16 6
17 6
18 7
19 7
20 01:10
21 40
22 25
23 45
24 30
25 52
26 20
27 25
28 250
29 30
30 2.5 or $2\frac{1}{2}$

Paper 16

 1 (eight o'clock)

 2 (twenty to four)

 3 (ten past five)

 4 (quarter to eleven)

5 5
6 8
7 3
8 4
9 3
10 5
11 9
12 11
13 9
14 16
15 14
16 22
17 60
18 40
19 26
20

Sunny							
Wet							
Dull							

21 3
22 5
23 2
24 21
25 44
26 58
27 24
28 28
29 27
30 30

Paper 17

1 £2.40
2 60p
3 crayons and eraser
4 £1.70
5 30p
6 £3.10
7 £1.95
8 felt tip pen set and scissors
9 43
10 42
11 66
12 447
13 69
14 100
15 456
16 378
17 48
18 6
19 12
20 6
21 18
22 $\frac{1}{2}$
23 $\frac{1}{4}$
24 $\frac{1}{4}$
25 21
26 50 min
27 20 min
28 30 miles
29 300 miles
30 600 miles

Paper 18

1 E
2 B
3 A
4 F
5 D
6 C
7 40
8 15
9 35
10 3×3
11 $10 + 1$
12 $3 + 2$
13 3456
14 7620
15 1389
16 9851
17 165
18 154
19 209

20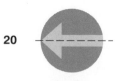

21

22

23 Yes
24 No
25 No
26 Yes
27 No
28 No
29 kg
30 15

Paper 19

1. 6.5
2. 11.5
3. 13
4. 9
5. 30 min
6. 9p
7. 20
8. 17
9. 18
10. 20
11. 21
12. Shaun
13. Zanna
14. Peter
15. Tim
16. Rachel
17. 100 m
18. 250 m
19. 500 m
20. 500 m
21. 800 m

22.

23.

24. 50 min
25. 1 hr 30 min or 90 min
26. 43
27. 20
28. 19
29. 8
30. 5

Paper 20

1. 06:20
2. 07:30
3. 08:40
4. 09:55
5. 11:00
6. $\frac{3}{4}$
7. $\frac{1}{4}$
8. $\frac{1}{2}$
9. $\frac{1}{4}$
10. $\frac{1}{2}$
11. $\frac{1}{4}$
12. 2
13. 7
14. 6
15. 26
16. 5 + 2
17. 11 + 2
18. 15 × 1
19. 3 × 6
20. 8 + 11
21. 0.5
22. 2
23. 1.5
24. 1
25. 2.5
26. 4.5
27. 4
28. 3
29. 07:45
30. 03:15

Paper 21

1. 7
2. 6
3. 6
4. 5
5. 5
6. 6
7. 340
8. 540
9. 900
10. 350
11. 189
12. 298
13. 13
14. 01:15
15. 16 days
16. £3.37
17. £3.87
18. £3.88
19. £7.90
20. 20
21. 18
22. 21
23. 18
24. 17
25. B
26. D
27. 1.5 kg
28. 5.5 kg
29. 4.5 kg
30. 20 weeks

1–6

Shapes

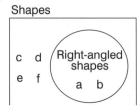

7 e
8 f
9 a
10 b
11 c
12 24
13 >
14 <
15 >
16 >

17

18

19

20

21

22

23

24

25 10
26 1
27 7
28 3
29

Seaside	👤	👤	👤	👤	👤	👤	👤	👤	
Camp	👤	👤	👤						
Farm	👤								
Abroad	👤	👤	👤	👤	👤	👤	👤		
Touring	👤	👤	👤	👤					

30 1007

Answers

15 Put a ring round any number that is a multiple of 3 and 5.

28   35   36   25   15

16 $30 \times 10 =$ _____

17 $4 \times 10 =$ _____

18 $600 \div 10 =$ _____

19 $50 \div 10 =$ _____

20 If 4 ice creams cost £3.00, what is the cost of one? _____

21 How much would 5 ice creams cost? _____

22 Annabel is 2 years older than Mary. Mary was born in 1996.
Annabel was born in the year _____

23–26 Fill in the missing numbers to make the scales balance.

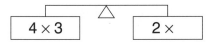

27–30 Write down the time shown on each clock below.

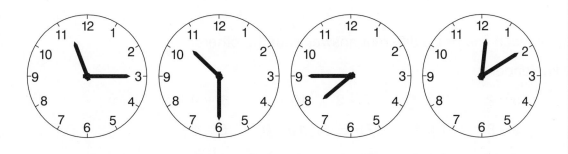

____ : ____ a.m.   ____ : ____ p.m.   ____ : ____ a.m.   ____ : ____ p.m.

Paper 12

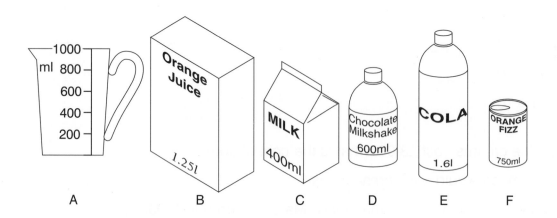

A   B   C   D   E   F

1 If the jug is half full how many ml are in it?   _____ ml

2 How many containers hold over a litre?   _____

3 If E was half full how much would it contain?   _____ ml

4–5 Which two containers when emptied would,
together, fill the measuring jug?   _____ and _____

6 If another container holds 200 ml how many times
could I fill it from a full jug?   _____

|6|

Put a ring round the highest number and draw a line under the smallest
number on each line.

7–8	79	76	77	97	67
9–10	64	87	46	68	78
11–12	55	53	54	35	45

|6|

One sum in each line has a different answer from the others.

Draw a line under it.

13	5×2	10×1	$12 - 2$	$10 + 1$	$6 + 4$
14	$9 - 8$	1×1	$7 - 6$	$10 - 9$	$6 - 4$
15	$4 \div 2$	$2 + 1$	2×1	$8 - 6$	$4 - 2$
16	2×1	3×1	$2 + 1$	$5 - 2$	$6 - 3$

|4|

17 80 – 30 = _____

18 20 + 50 = _____

19 100 – 40 = _____

Here is part of a ruler. Look at it and then answer the questions.

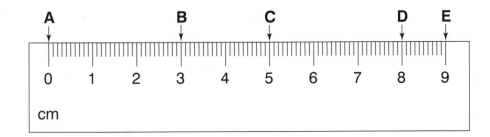

20 How far is it from A to B? _____ cm

21 From A to C is _____ cm.

22 From B to D is _____ cm.

23 From C to E is _____ cm.

Fill in the missing digits.

24 47 – 2_____ = 21

25 38 – 2_____ = 13

26 _____7 – 25 = 22

27 74 – _____3 = 51

Find a pair of numbers with:

28 a sum of 9 and a product of 18. _____ and _____

29 a sum of 12 and a product of 11. _____ and _____

30 a sum of 12 and a product of 36. _____ and _____

Paper 13

1–7 Draw a line between each of these shapes and its name.

rectangle

pyramid

cube

cone

cuboid

triangle

square

Put a ring round the highest number and draw a line under the lowest number on each line.

8–9	24	23	34	32	43
10–11	19	71	77	29	17
12–13	31	35	36	53	33

Put a sign in each space to make the sum correct.

14 3 _____ 5 = 8

15 9 _____ 2 = 7

16 2 _____ 4 = 8

Draw all the lines of symmetry in these shapes.

17

18

19

20 Alison will be 5 in 2005. In what year was she born? _____

What **fraction** of each of these shapes is shaded and what fraction is white?

21–22 Shaded _____

  White _____

23–24 Shaded _____

  White _____

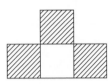

25–26 Shaded _____

  White _____

27–28 Shaded _____

  White _____

8

29 What is the lowest number you can make with these digits:

4, 7, 2? _____

30 Now write it in words. _____

2

30
TOTAL

Paper 14

Here is an easy way to work out 14 × 8.

×	10	4
8	80	32	= 112

Now do these multiplications in the same way.

1 13 × 8

×	10	
8			= ____

2 15×6

$\times$ 10

6   [|]   = _____

3 18×6

$\times$ 10

[|]   = _____

4 19×5

$\times$

[|]   = _____

5 17×6

$\times$

[|]   = _____

6 15×9

$\times$

[|]   = _____

6

7–12 Fill in the missing numbers to make the scales balance.

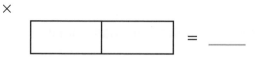

| 20 − 4 | △ | 2 × |

| 30 − | △ | 4 × 5 |

| 15 + | △ | 5 × 5 |

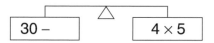

| 10 + | △ | 5 × 3 |

| 16 ÷ 4 | △ | 9 − |

| 3 × 3 | △ | 12 − |

6

13 Giles has 20 socks. If he puts them in pairs he will have _____ pairs.

14 How much must I add to 65p to make £1.00?   _____ p

15 What number is one less than 1000? _____ | 3 |

There is one digit missing from each of these sums.

Can you find what it is? Write it in the space.

16
```
    2   4
+   1 ____
_____
    3   7
```

17
```
    3 ____
+   2   4
_____
    5   9
```

18
```
    2   5
+   1 ____
_____
    3   7
```

19
```
  ____  6
+   2   3
_____
    6   9
```
| 4 |

20 Graham had 40p. He bought two erasers and had only 2p left. This means that one eraser costs _____ p.

21 How many minutes are there in a quarter of an hour? _____ | 2 |

Use your ruler to measure these lines in centimetres.

22 _____

23 _____

24 _____

25 _____

26 _____

27 _____
| 6 |

There are 51 children altogether in Classes 1 and 2.

28 If there are 26 in Class 1 how many are there in Class 2? _____

29 Write one hundred and two in figures. _____

30 Write one hundred and twenty in figures. _____
| 3 |

| 30 |
| TOTAL |

Paper 15

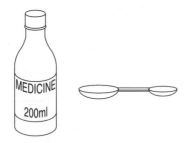

The medicine spoon has two ends. One end can measure 5 ml. The other end can measure 10 ml.

1 If the bottle is full how many doses of 10 ml are in the bottle?

_____

2 When the bottle is half full how many ml are in it?   _____ ml

3 If the bottle is half full how many doses of 5 ml are in the bottle?

_____

Another much larger spoon holds 20 ml.

4 How many times can you fill this spoon from the full bottle?_____

4

What fraction of each of these shapes is shaded and what fraction is white?

5–6   Shaded   _____

White   _____

7–8   Shaded   _____

White   _____

9–10   Shaded   _____

White   _____

11–12   Shaded   _____

White   _____

8

Put a sign in each question to make it correct.

13 4 _____ 4 = 16   **14** 7 _____ 2 = 5   **15** 3 _____ 0 = 0 | 3 |

Here are some questions on **rounding up** or **down**.

We know that 37 ÷ 6 = 6 remainder 1.

16 I have 37 eggs. One egg box holds 6 eggs.

   I could fill only _____ egg boxes.

17 I have £37. Cinema tickets cost £6 each.

   I could only buy _____ tickets.

18 I have 37 eggs. One egg box holds 6 eggs.

   I will need _____ egg boxes to hold all 37 eggs.

19 I have 37 guests coming for a special dinner.

   My tables can only seat 6 people each.

   _____ tables are needed to seat all the guests. | 4 |

20 Paul's watch is 5 minutes fast. It shows 01:15.

   What is the right time?   _____ : _____ | 1 |

Here is a train timetable.

	Train A	Train B	Train C	Train D
Leaves Rigby	09:00	10:05	11:15	12:10
Arrives in Stairs	09:40	10:30	12:00	12:40

21 Train A takes _____ min.   **22** Train B takes _____ min.

23 Train C takes _____ min.   **24** Train D takes _____ min. | 4 |

25 What number is five tens and a two?   _____

26 What number is three fours and an eight?   _____ | 2 |

27 What number is half way between 20 and 30?   _____

28 What number is half way between 200 and 300? _____

29 What number is half way between 25 and 35? _____

30 What number is half way between 2 and 3? _____

Paper 16

1–4 Draw hands on each of the clocks below to show the correct time.

Make sure you put the small hand in the right place.

8 o'clock

Twenty to four

Ten past five

Quarter to eleven

Do you remember how to do these sums from Paper 5? Now do these.

5 $5 \times \clubsuit = 25$

$\clubsuit$ = _____

6 $2 \times \heartsuit = 16$

$\heartsuit$ = _____

7 $3 \times \spadesuit = 9$

$\spadesuit$ = _____

8 $3 \times \bullet = 10 + 2$

$\bullet$ = _____

9 $5 \times \Phi = 15$

Φ = _____

10 $2 \times \clubsuit = 8 + 2$

$\clubsuit$ = _____

11–16 Annabel is 5 years older than Nicholas.

Fill in the missing ages in the chart below.

When Nicholas is	4	6		11		17
Annabel is			14		19	

Underline the correct answer in each line.

17 $600 \div 10 =$ 6   60   600   6000

18 $5 \times 8 =$ 58   35   40   45

19 $17 + 9 =$ 26   27   29   25

3

Last year Tom went to stay on a farm. He was away for 14 days.

He made this chart to show what the weather was like. He has not filled in the entries for dull days. Each square represents 1 day.

Sunny							
Wet							
Dull							

20 Draw on the chart the number of days it was dull.

21 How many more days were dull than were wet?   _____

22 How many more days were sunny than were wet?   _____

23 How many more days were sunny than were dull?   _____   4

Fill in the missing number in each line.

24   18   _____   24   27   30

25   29   34   39   _____   49

26   18   28   38   48   _____   3

27–30 Here are the marks some children got in their tests. Find each child's total marks.

	Paul	Tim	Carmen	Julie
Test 1	7	8	5	9
Test 2	4	7	7	8
Test 3	6	4	8	6
Test 4	7	9	7	7
Totals				

4

30
TOTAL

Paper 17

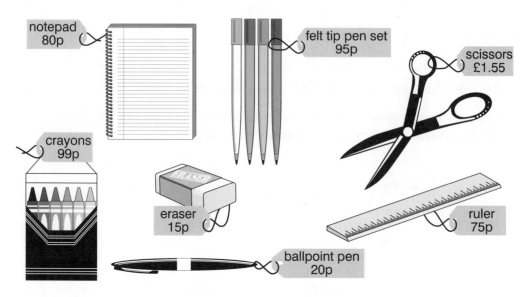

notepad 80p

felt tip pen set 95p

scissors £1.55

crayons 99p

eraser 15p

ruler 75p

ballpoint pen 20p

1 I bought 3 notepads. What did I pay? _____

2 How much change did I get from £3.00? _____

3 Which 2 things can I buy for £1.14 exactly? _____ and _____

4 Dad bought a notepad, an eraser and a ruler.
   Together they cost _____

5 How much change did Dad get from £2.00? _____

6 How much do two pairs of scissors cost?
   (Remember one pair of scissors is one item.) _____

7 How much would it cost to buy 2 ballpoint pens
   and a pair of scissors? _____

8 Which 2 things would cost £2.50 exactly?

_____

| 8 |

9   60   10   70   11   80
       − 17   − 28   − 14
     ───────   ───────   ───────

     ───────   ───────   ───────

| 3 |

12 347 + 100 = _____   13   59 + 10 = _____

36

14   90 + 10 = _____   **15**   356 + 100 = _____

16   478 – 100 = _____   **17**   58 – 10 = _____

Here is a **pictogram** showing which summer sports children in Class 3A like best.

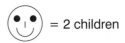 = 2 children

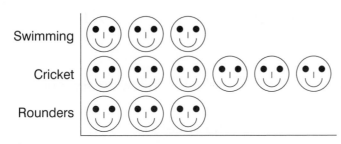

No of children

18 How many like swimming best? _____

19 How many like cricket best? _____

20 How many like rounders best? _____

21 How many did not choose rounders? _____

22 What fraction of the class likes cricket best? _____

23 What fraction of the class likes swimming best? _____

24 What fraction of the class likes rounders best? _____

25 What is the sum of 6, 7 and 8? _____

26 The film lasted 53 minutes, which is _____ to the nearest 10 min.

27 The big chocolate bar lasted 16 minutes, which is _____ to the nearest 10 min.

28 Oxton to Muleton is 27 miles, which is _____ to the nearest 10 miles.

29 Mondon to Meeds is 283 miles, which is _____ to the nearest 100 miles.

30 The return trip (Mondon to Meeds and back) is _____ to the nearest 100 miles.

Paper 18

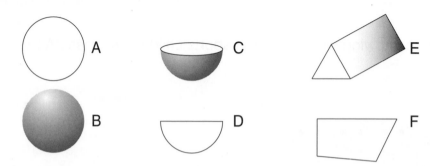

Put the letters A to F in the correct spaces to make the following sentences true.

1 _____ is a prism.

2 The sphere is _____.

3 _____ is a circle.

4 The **quadrilateral** is _____.

5 _____ is a semicircle.

6 The hemisphere is _____.

How many minutes are there between:

7 [clock] and (11:40) _____ min   8 (10:35) and [clock] _____ min

9 [clock] and (12:45) _____ min

One question on each line has a different answer from the others.

Put a line under it.

10	7 + 1	4 × 2	8 × 1	3 × 3	6 + 2
11	2 × 5	11 − 1	10 + 1	10 × 1	4 + 6
12	3 + 2	6 × 1	3 × 2	7 − 1	4 + 2

13 What is the smallest number you can make with these digits: 5, 3, 6, 4? _____

14 What is the biggest number you can make with these digits: 2, 0, 6, 7? _____

15 What is the smallest number you can make with these digits: 1, 9, 3, 8? _____

38

16 What is the biggest number you can make with these digits: 5, 1, 8, 9? _____ | 4 |

Here is an easy way to work out 16 × 11.

×	10	1	
16	160	16	= 176

Now do these the same way.

17 15 × 11   ×

		= _____

18 11 × 14   ×

		= _____

19 11 × 19   ×

		= _____

| 3 |

Draw all the lines of symmetry (mirror lines) in these shapes.

20    **21**    **22**

| 3 |

Is it possible to do the following sums? Write 'Yes' or 'No'.

23 4 cm + 2 m +17 cm _____   **24** 5 m + 4 l + 5 l _____

25 4 km + 2 kg + 3 km _____   **26** 8 kg + 20 g + 27 g _____

27 40 ml + 21 g + 5 ml _____   **28** 3 cm – 11 ml + 5 ml _____

| 6 |

29 Choose the best unit of measure from the above to measure the weight of a man. _____ | 1 |

30 What is the sum of the numbers 1 to 5? _____ | 1 |

39

| 30 |
| TOTAL |

Paper 19

Measure the lengths of these things.

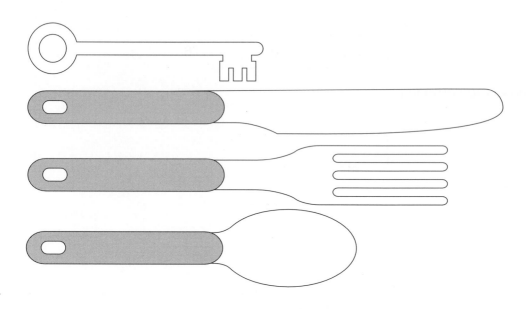

1 The key is _____ cm long.   2 The fork is _____ cm long.

3 The knife is _____ cm long.   4 The spoon is _____ cm long. `4`

5 A lesson started at ten minutes to two and finished at twenty minutes past two.

   How long did the lesson last?   _____ `1`

6 What must I add to 16p to make 25p?   _____ `1`

Here are the marks some children scored in a test.

7–11 Add them up.

	Peter	Zanna	Tim	Rachel	Shaun
	6	7	8	6	7
	5	4	7	6	8
	9	6	3	8	6
Totals					

12 Who had the highest total mark? _____

13 Who had the lowest total mark? _____

14 Who got the highest mark in any one test? _____

15 Who got the lowest mark in any one test? _____

16 Who got the same mark in two tests? _____ | 10 |

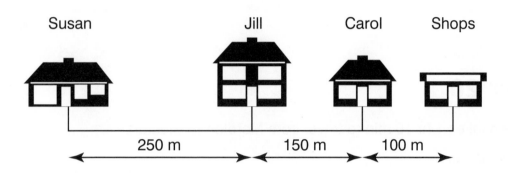

Susan   Jill   Carol   Shops

250 m   150 m   100 m

17 How far does Carol live from the shops? _____

18 How far does Jill have to walk to the shops? _____

19 How far does Susan live from the shops? _____

20 If Jill walked to Susan's house and then home again how far would she walk? _____

21 If Susan walked to Carol's house and then home again how far would she walk? _____ | 5 |

Draw all the lines of symmetry (mirror lines) in these shapes.

22

23

| 2 |

24 It takes James 46 minutes to clean a car inside and out, which is _____ to the nearest 10 min.

25 How long will it take James to clean two cars to the nearest 10 min?

_____ | 2 |

26 What number is four tens and three? _____

27 What number is three sixes and two? _____

28 What number is five threes and four? _____ | 3

29–30 Find a pair of numbers with a sum of 13 and a product of 40.

_____ and _____ | 2

| 30 |
| TOTAL |

Paper 20

1–5 A train takes 1 hr 10 min to travel from Moreton to Bidston.

Fill in the timetable.

	Train A	Train B	Train C	Train D
Leaves Moreton	05:10	06:20	08:45	09:50
Arrives at Bidston				

| 5 |

What fraction of each shape is shaded?

6 ___    **7** ___ 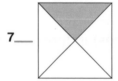   **8** ___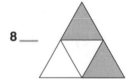

9 ___    **10** ___    **11** ___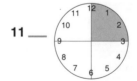

| 6 |

Find the missing digits.

12
```
  3 ___
+ 1   4
───────
  4   6
───────
```

13
```
  1   9
-   ___
───────
  1   2
───────
```

14
```
      4   2
  ×       3
───────────
  1 2 ___
───────────
```

| 3 |

42

15 What is half of 52? _____ | 1 |

Underline the incorrect answer in each line.

16	10 =	6 + 4	3 + 7	5 + 2	10 × 1
17	12 =	11 + 2	6 + 6	4 + 8	2 × 6
18	16 =	2 × 8	4 × 4	17 − 1	15 × 1
19	15 =	7 + 8	3 × 6	9 + 6	15 ÷ 1
20	18 =	8 + 11	12 + 6	3 × 6	2 × 9

| 5 |

This drawing shows part of a centimetre ruler. Look at it and then answer the questions.

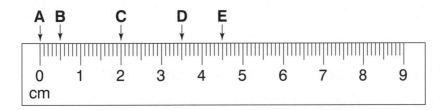

21 How far is it from A to B? _____ cm

22 From A to C is _____ cm

23 From C to D is _____ cm

24 D to E is _____ cm

25 How far is it from C to E? _____ cm

26 From A to E is _____ cm

27 From B to E is _____ cm

28 From B to D is _____ cm | 8 |

29 We will have our breakfast in a quarter of an hour. It is now 07:30. When will we have breakfast? _____ : _____

30 It is a quarter to four. What time was it half an hour ago? _____ : _____ | 2 |

| 30 |
| TOTAL |

Paper 21

1–6 Fill in the spaces to make the scales balance.

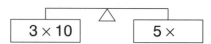

17 – [ ] △ 3 × 4

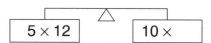

6

7 What is the multiple of 10 that follows 340? _____

8 What is the multiple of 10 that comes before 550? _____

9 What is the multiple of 100 that follows 800? _____

10 What is the multiple of 5 that comes before 345? _____

11 What odd number comes before 191? _____

12 What even number comes before 300? _____

13 What number is 4 more than 3 × 3? _____

14 My watch is 5 minutes slow.
If it shows 10 minutes past 1 what is the right time? ____ : ____

15 My dog eats 4 biscuits a day.
How long will a packet of 64 biscuits last him? _____

9

16   £1.24
     + £2.13
     _____

     _____

17   £2.43
     + £1.45
     _____

     _____

18   £3.61
     + £2.27
     _____

     _____

19   £4.25
     + £3.65
     _____

     _____

4

Five children took part in the school sports day.
Each time they came first they were given 5 points.
Each time they came second they were given 3 points.
Each time they came third they were given 1 points.

20–24 Fill in the total number of points each child was given.

	1st	2nd	3rd	Total
Keith	✔✔	✔✔✔	✔	
Maria	✔✔✔	✔		
Martin	✔✔✔	✔	✔✔✔	
Tanya	✔✔	✔✔	✔✔	
Ian	✔	✔✔✔	✔✔✔	

5

25 Which is the heaviest parcel? _____

26 Which is the lightest parcel? _____

27 How much heavier is B than A? _____

28 How much lighter is D than E? _____

29 How much heavier is E than C? _____

5

30 I save 50p each week.
How long will it take me to save £10.00? _____

1

30
TOTAL

45

Paper 22

1–6 Put the letters **a** to **f** in the correct place in the Venn diagram.

Shapes

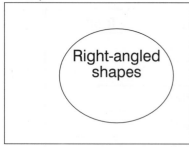

 a

 b

 c

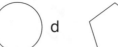 d

 e

 f

7–8 Which shapes have an odd number of edges? _____ and _____

9–11 Which shapes have an even number of vertices?

_____ and _____ and _____

11

12 A dinner lady puts 4 rows of pasties in the oven. There are 6 pasties on each of 4 rows.

How many pasties does she bake? _____

1

This sign < means less than and this sign > means greater than.

Put one of these signs in each of the spaces below.

13 (7 + 2) _____ 8

14 (5 + 4) _____ 10

15 (2 + 6) _____ 7

16 (3 + 5) _____ 6

4

Here are some clocks of the things Paolo did last Saturday.

Draw the hands of each clock, taking care to put them on the right numbers.

17 Paolo got up at 7:45.

18 He had breakfast at 8:30.

19 He went to football at 9:10.

20 He had lunch at 2:05.

21 Paolo went shopping with his mum at 2:40.

22 He ate again at 5:25.

23 He played on the computer at 6:20.

24 He went to bed at 8:35.

8

There are 25 children in the class. They made this chart to show how they are going to spend their holidays.

Seaside	👤	👤	👤	👤	👤	👤	👤	👤	👤	👤
Camp	👤	👤	👤							
Farm	👤									
Abroad	👤	👤	👤	👤	👤	👤	👤			
Touring										

👤 = 1 person

25 How many are going to the seaside? _____

26 How many are going to a farm? _____

27 How many children are going abroad? _____

28 How many are going to camp? _____

29 Fill in on the chart the number of children who are touring.

5

30 Write one thousand and seven in figures. _____

1

30
TOTAL

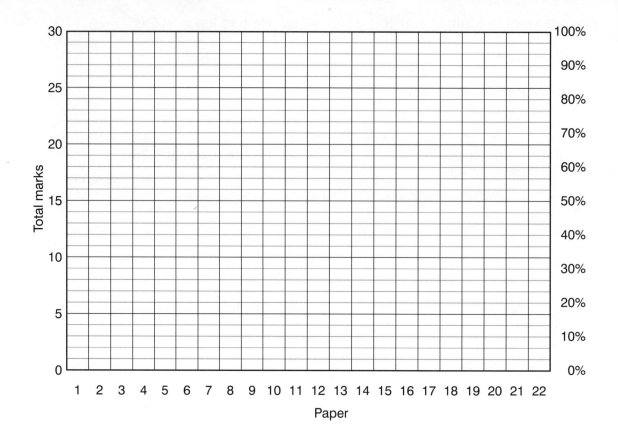